The children were doing a project on
the Olympic Games.

"Tomorrow we will go to the museum and
next week it's sports day," said Mrs May.

"Everyone can enter a race on sports day," said Mrs May.

"I think the girls should have a sewing race!" laughed one of the boys.

After school, Anneena and Wilma went
to play with Biff. Anneena was cross.
"Some boys are so silly," she said.
The magic key began to glow.

The magic took the girls back in time, to
a village in Greece. A boy was calling to
the villagers.

"Follow me to the games," he said.

"Can we go too?" asked Biff.

"Anyone can come!" said the boy. "As long as they are male."

The men and the boys from the village went to the games.

"It's not fair!" said Anneena.

"Let's follow them," said Biff.

Outside the games, there were lots of guards. They only let men and boys in to the games.

"We'll never get in," said Biff.

"I wish we could see!" said Wilma.
Anneena had an idea. "Let's climb
a tree," she said.

The girls climbed an olive tree.
They could see the games. They watched
a race. Lots of men ran with shields.

The winner won a prize. The prize
was a vase. A man put a crown on the
winner's head.

Then the girls watched some men
throwing discs as far as they could.
"Hey you!" shouted a girl.

The girl was under the tree.
"If anyone catches you here, you'll be
in for the high jump!" she said.

"Then, why are you here?" asked Biff.
"I'm picking olives," said the girl.
"My name is Hera. You'd better come with
me to the village."

In the village, they met Hera's
friend, Mila.

"It's always quiet when the games
are on," said Mila. "It's so boring!"

Suddenly, Anneena had an idea.
"Can you get all of your friends
together?" she asked.

The girls in the village came to
the meeting.

"This is my grandmother," said Mila.
"She paints the vases for the games."

"Listen everyone," said Anneena.
"Why should boys have all the fun?
Let's have a girls' Olympic Games!"

There were all sorts of races and
all the girls took part. There was a
three-legged race and a sack race.

Mila's grandmother gave the girls
some old plates. The girls threw them
like discs. They threw them as far as
they could.

The girls had an olive-and-spoon race. Biff dropped her olives and Hera slipped on them!

Mila's grandmother painted the girls on a vase. Hera made some crowns from olive twigs.

"We're all winners!" she said.

The boys and the men came back.

"Girls doing sports?" said one boy.

"That will never catch on!"

Suddenly, the magic key began to glow.

The next day, Mrs May took the class to the museum. There was a display about the Greek Olympics. In a glass case there was a broken vase.

"A long time ago, a girls' Olympics began," said Mrs May.

Anneena looked at the boys. "And did the idea catch on?" she asked.